My Name Is RACHAMIM

Jonathan P. Kendall

Illustrated by
Alemu Eshetie

Union of American Hebrew Congregations ◆ *New York*

For Jessica Rachel and Rebecca Ann
who share in the delight
that Rachamim and his family
are finally home

Publication of this book
has been made possible by
The Blum Family Publication Fund
Max and the late Ida
Helene and the late Sidney

Acknowledgments

Special thanks to my secretary, Lynnette Pennings, who continually typed, revised, and edited the manuscript; to Aron Hirt-Manheimer for his support and advice; to Ina Block who, with a late-night telephone call, started me on a path which led to "Operation Moses" and eventually to Rachamim; and to Jo Beth for her unflagging love, loyalty, devotion, and encouragement.

Introduction

No one knows the origin of the Beta Esrael (House of Israel), as Jews of Ethiopia call themselves. Some believe they may be a remnant from the lost tribe of Dan. They themselves say that their history begins with Menelik, a son of Solomon, who led their ancestors to Ethiopia from ancient Israel.

What we do know about the Beta Esrael is that for centuries they have been cut off from other Jewish communities. Because of this the Judaism they practice is completely different from anything we know today. Their Judaism was never exposed to the Mishnah, the Talmud, the great editors of Jewish law and practice, the glories of Spain, or the *yeshivot* of Eastern Europe; in short, the Judaism they practice is probably the purest biblical Judaism there is. Their isolation also led them to believe that they were the only surviving Jewish community left on earth. They were shocked when confronted with white Jews who spoke Yiddish or Ladino or only Hebrew.

Somehow, despite hundreds of years of forced conversions, torture, slavery, and pogroms, they preserved their Judaism in a hostile environment. In a land where personal hygiene was unheard of, they bore the name "the people who smell like water" because they bathed before each Shabbat and after coming into contact with outsiders. Family life was remarkably stable. Piety and humility were the two most prevalent personal characteristics.

Their non-Jewish neighbors called them *Falasha*, which means "alien" or "stranger" in Amharic. Because they were viewed as outsiders, they enjoyed few rights, no security, and little respect. Even into this decade, their young men and women were being sold into slavery and sometimes murdered because they were Jews. But their devotion to Judaism kept them alive.

As the famine in Ethiopia grew worse, American Jewish and Israeli interest in the fate of the Beta Esrael became more intense. On a November evening in 1984, I received a telephone call from a friend who often keeps me informed on important Jewish events in Israel and around the world. She said, "I can't go into any details, but I can tell you we're getting them out." For the next three months, I traveled around the country, raising funds for what came to be known as "Operation Moses," the secret transport and resettling of the Beta Esrael in Israel.

At the end of these three months, I went to Israel to see for myself what this massive resettlement program had accomplished. I've been back twice since, and tears still come to my eyes when I think of the hundreds of Beta Esrael who perished from hunger and disease in the stifling Sudanese refugee camps. As many as twelve hundred may have died in the Sudan from hunger and disease.

Their transition to modern life in Israel has not been easy. Ethiopian Jews have had their Jewish identity questioned by Orthodox religious authorities, particularly in matters of marriage and divorce. Adjustment for some has been difficult, especially for those who left behind family among the 8,000–10,000 Beta Esrael still in Ethiopia with no means of escape. The younger generation, however, is having no trouble integrating into Israeli society.

In my travels I met many young people who had contributed their *tsedakah* or *keren ami* money to help the Beta Esrael escape to Israel. They were among those who made it possible for the Beta Esrael to be lifted up on eagles' wings and brought home to Zion. When *their* children ask them, "What truly important thing have you done?" they can say, "I helped save a life, a Jewish life." Maybe even Rachamim's.

Jonathan P. Kendall
Santa Barbara, California

My name is Rachamim. I was born in a village in Ethiopia, in an area called the Gondar. When I think of where I was born, I smile. There were rolling hills and wide, beautiful rivers near my home. I never imagined that one day my family would have to leave this beautiful place.

Ever since any of us can remember, my people have lived in the Gondar. We built our homes atop a hill so that we could see anyone approaching. We lived by a river so that we could water our cattle and sheep and irrigate our corn, grains, and vegetables.

My father, Gideon, and my mother, Rakael, worked as blacksmiths. With fire and metal, they fashioned tools and pots and objects of beauty to decorate homes. When they could afford to buy a little gold or silver, they made jewelry—fine necklaces and bracelets which they sold in the city of Gondar, about a day's walk from our village. My parents were more than blacksmiths, they were artists.

◆　◆　◆　◆　◆

I have two younger brothers, Menelik and Moshe. They are named after two great heroes of our people. Menelik, a son of King Solomon, led my people to the Gondar long ago. I guess everyone knows who Moshe is; he led our people out of slavery in Egypt. My two little sisters, Rivkah and Leah, are named after two very important women in our history. Rivkah was Isaac's wife; Leah was the first wife of Jacob.

My brothers, sisters, and I had many playmates and often ran around our village in games of hide-and-seek, tag, and soccer. Or we sat on the ground around an older person who told us wonderful stories. I loved to hear about brave kings and huge temples that almost touched the sky, about God, and, most of all, about a place where all of us would go someday, lifted up on the wings of eagles, a place called "Zion."

◆ ◆ ◆ ◆ ◆

When I think back to those peaceful days in our village, I remember Friday mornings. I can still smell the lamb stew my mother made for the special celebration we held every seventh Friday and the flat bread she baked every week.

Later, we would all go to the river to bathe, then return home to our *tukul* and put on fresh clothes. We would eat our last hot

meal around four o'clock in the afternoon. As the sky went from a clear blue to red and orange, our whole village gathered together and wished each other "*Sanbat Salaam*," our Shabbat greeting in Amharic. No one was allowed to work, light a fire, walk a great distance, or play a game, for this was God's holy *Sanbat*, brought to us from heaven by angels.

Our prayers tell us, "They who honor the *Sanbat* are as if they honor God. They who make the *Sanbat* a day of delight are considered as if they made a loan to God." The *Sanbat* is the holy day of rest, which God gave to the Jewish people, to us, the Beta Esrael.

◆ ◆ ◆ ◆ ◆

On *Sanbat* you would find all of us in our *mesgid*, a big *tukul* with two rooms. The larger, outer room was used for prayer. On the *Sanbat* our *kes* led the people in prayer, saying, "*Adonai* is One."

After finishing the reading in the holy books, the *kes* or his helper, the *dabtara*, put them away in the second room of the *mesgid* called the "Holy of Holies," which only a *kes* or a *dabtara* might enter.

◆ ◆ ◆ ◆ ◆

I was happy in the Gondar, but being a Jew there was often difficult. For centuries, people of other faiths have wanted us to change from our ways to theirs. Our *kes* told us of many ancient battles when the Beta Esrael were tortured, carried off as slaves, or even killed because we refused to give up our faith in *Adonai* as the One and Only God.

But no matter what was done to us, we never stopped being Jews. We knew that someday our prayers would be answered. When the *kes* told us about these things, we would all say together, "This is the One who lifted me up from the gates of death so that I might tell God's praises in the gates of the daughters of Zion."

◆   ◆   ◆   ◆   ◆

But then one year the big rains did not come. The once proud river became too shallow for our *Sanbat* bath. Then it disappeared. Without water, there was no grain for my mother to grind, no corn or vegetables to cook. The animals dropped to the ground, and many of them died. Where there was once rich soil, now dust swirled in a hot and biting wind. There was no work for anyone. I watched my friends get thinner and thinner. My little sisters were always sick. Menelik and Moshe were always crying, crying for food. I felt like crying too.

During those days of famine our *kes* spoke of returning to Zion. Perhaps the drought and the hunger were signs from *Adonai*. The green hills were now brown. The sun, once our friend, was now our enemy. I prayed and searched the sky for eagles.

◆   ◆   ◆   ◆   ◆

Our *tukul* had always been filled with laughter. But now my father brooded. No longer did he work every day; he just sat, day after day, with empty hands.

Once in a while, he would take my hand and walk with me around our village. We walked through what used to be our fields and down to the banks of what used to be the river.

"Remember the flowing river," he said. "Remember the green hills and the happy times we spent here. Remember them, Rachamim, because I am afraid they are gone forever. Remember that we have lived here for longer than anyone knows. We have been here since King Solomon sat on the throne of Israel. The blood of King David runs in our veins. Always remember." I said that I would remember, but in my heart I didn't understand what he was trying to tell me. Again and again he repeated the words, "We gave the Torah to the world. Through fire and torture and slavery, we were always the Beta Esrael, a proud and special people." I went to sleep that night very confused—and very hungry.

◆　◆　◆　◆　◆

Have you ever gone to bed hungry? Night after night I dreamt about food. Then one night at the height of the famine I dreamt it was the seventh *Sanbat* and my plate was filled with lamb stew. I brought it to my lips and…I awoke to my mother's voice.

"Everything we can carry is packed," she said.

"Where are we going?" I asked.

My father answered, "Tonight we will leave this place forever. Tonight we begin our journey home."

When we walked out of our *tukul*, I saw everyone from our village lined up, carrying their most important things. Some had pots and pans, others carried clothes or bedding, some were so weak they leaned on each other.

"How far is home?" I asked.

"Very far," said my mother. "We must walk a long and dangerous road, but, when we get there, we will be safe."

◆   ◆   ◆   ◆   ◆

We walked for two weeks, sleeping during the day and traveling at night. The sun was so strong and there was so little food and water that, if we had tried to walk during the day, we would have perished. The way we went was filled with robbers and thieves who were ready to steal what little we had. And we had to watch out for soldiers who tried to stop us from leaving Ethiopia. We hid during the day, fearing for our lives.

At night, by moonlight, we followed our *kes* through deserts which were drier than the river bed we left behind. We walked through valleys over rocks that tore our sandals and bruised our feet. We walked through brush that ripped our clothes and scratched our bodies. Only on the *Sanbat* did we stop to rest.

Just before dawn one morning we walked over a small hill and saw hundreds of tents and campfires stretching to the horizon. I was so tired and hungry and excited that I said, "Now we are home!" My father put his arm around me and told me that we still had a long way to go, but we would stay for a while in this land called the Sudan.

◆　◆　◆　◆　◆

We were in a camp which held many thousands of people, all of them from Ethiopia, but only a few Beta Esrael. We did not tell anyone who we were because we were afraid that others might harm us. For many years our Ethiopian neighbors had treated us badly. Now we were all thrown together in a strange land, living in tents. Ours was so flimsy that a strong wind could blow it down. For months we lived in fear.

We had to be very careful about the food we ate because a Beta Esrael may eat food prepared only by another Jew, according to the laws of our sacred books. But food and water were scarce. Days became weeks, and some of our people died. We couldn't even bury them in the way Judaism demands for fear of exposing ourselves as Jews. Our bodies already hurt. Now our hearts ached too.

♦ ♦ ♦ ♦ ♦

How terrible it was in that camp: dust and flies, a smell that never went away, sickness and death. It was like living a nightmare. But, just when I thought it would never end, a man came to our tent. He was dressed like everyone else, hardly any clothes at all, but he was clean underneath those rags and he was well fed. He spoke our language and introduced himself as Yaakov. "Be ready tonight!" he told us.

As it grew darker, the people who were left from my village slowly walked out of the camp. I asked my father, "Are we finally going home to Zion?" He didn't answer but held my hand and led me to where Yaakov was standing with other men near trucks. I had seen such vehicles before, but I had never been inside one. I was glad we could ride. I was getting too weak to walk.

We bumped along the road until dawn. When finally the trucks stopped, I couldn't believe what I saw.

At the edge of a clearing stood a great, silver bird with gleaming metal wings. There was a stairway from the ground to a door in the side of this shining bird, and people from all directions were walking up and disappearing inside. We joined them. Where would this great eagle take us? People ahead of us were pushing and some were laughing, but I could tell they were scared; they laughed too much.

We all sat down in soft seats. Some people were chattering away, others sat silently. Strangers walked up and down the center of the plane, strapping us into our seats and handing us water to drink. Some of them were white people who spoke Amharic.

When they closed the doors, I began to tremble. With a roar louder than any thunder we had ever heard, the eagle began to move. It went faster and faster until all of a sudden I felt as if we had fallen off the earth. I looked out the window and saw trees and hills rush by.

My father and mother sat with their eyes shut. My brothers and sisters cried. So did I. But then, exhausted, I fell asleep. When I awoke, I looked down and saw water everywhere. Someone said it was the Mediterranean Sea. We flew for a long time. Some people prayed, others slept, some were full of questions, some were too sick to do more than sit and stare.

The plane finally began to go down. My ears hurt, and someone handed me my first piece of gum! The earth rushed up and suddenly we were on the ground.

◆ ◆ ◆ ◆ ◆

We landed in a strange land called Belgium and were moved to another airplane. I was cold as we walked to the new plane. The ground was covered with something cold and white. They told me it was *sheleg*, snow. That is all I remember about Belgium.

The second airplane was blue and white and had a six-pointed star on its tail. When we were all on board, people stood up and welcomed us in Amharic, but, among themselves, they spoke another language. I thought I recognized a few words, but they spoke so quickly that I couldn't follow most of it.

"What language are you speaking?" I asked.

"*Ivrit*," said one of the men. "Hebrew."

Can these people all be Jews, I thought? How is this possible? Are there white Jews? Is this a Jewish airplane? For hundreds of years, maybe thousands, we thought we were the only Jews left on earth. This was surely a sign from *Adonai*, a miracle!

The plane took off and flew through clouds as white as our *kes's Sanbat* clothes, over a large lake as blue as the skies of Gondar. I couldn't help staring at the white people on the plane. Imagine, white Jews!

The people from our village all sat together. But there were many more. Some came from villages and towns nearby. Others came all the way from Addis Ababa, the capital of Ethiopia. Some were well dressed; others looked like us, dressed only in rags. There were families like ours, children whose parents were dead or missing, parents whose children had died along the way. Above the roar of the engines, there were two hundred and fifty voices speaking, laughing, crying, moaning, praying, all at once.

Looking out of the window, I saw land in the distance. It was just a speck, but it was green and beautiful. Then there was a large and glistening city, its buildings reaching up from the edge of the lake and stretching as far as I could see. And then, like before, the trees and land rushed up and, with the sound of thunder, we landed.

The plane rolled to a stop, the door opened, and more white people entered. *"Shalom Aleichem, Shalom Aleichem,"* they said. "Peace unto you, peace unto you."

Our *kes* was the first to leave the plane. As he reached the bottom of the steps, he kneeled and kissed the ground. Grabbing Yaakov's hand, he said, "Like Moses, you have led your people home."

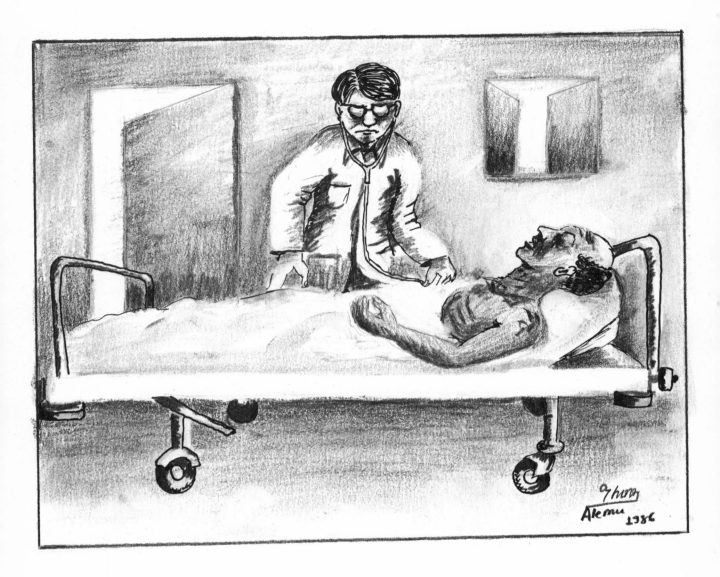

We left the plane and were taken to a large room. More people came to see us. Some of them, wearing white clothes, looked in our ears and eyes and throats. They listened to our breathing. They told us they were doctors and nurses.

Then we were put on trucks with windows—they called them buses—and off we drove onto streets with so many buses and trucks and bright lights that I had to close my eyes. All of these people couldn't be Jews, could they? But they *were*, and this was home.

The people of our village were given food and water, new clothes, and a place to live. Since we arrived in Israel, my family and I have learned Hebrew, the language that the Beta Esrael spoke when Solomon was king. My parents are learning a new trade because no one needs blacksmiths here. Our *dabtara* still teaches us about our proud history, and our *kes* still leads us in prayer. I miss our village and our *tukul*, the *mesgid* where we prayed, and the river where we washed for the *Sanbat*. I miss them—but not enough to want to go back.

I am glad to be here. When I am hungry or thirsty, there is plenty to eat and drink. We are safe here among our people. I have many new friends, some from Morocco, Iraq, France, Greece, and the United States—all of them Jews just like me, only a different color. They are happy to be here, too, to be home.

My name is Rachamim. Perhaps some day, if you visit this land, we will meet. I have so much more to tell, about the Beta Esrael, about being lifted up on eagles' wings, about coming home to Zion, to Israel.

Glossary

Amharic: The Semitic language that is the official language of Ethiopia.

Beta Esrael: House of Israel. The name the Jews of Ethiopia call themselves.

Dabtara: A reader, assistant to the priest, who has studied sacred texts but has not been ordained into the priesthood.

Falasha: The word for "alien," "stranger," or "exile" in *Amharic* (see above). This is the name by which non-Jews in Ethiopia refer to the Ethiopian Jews.

Keren Ami: Hebrew term meaning "the fund of my people." It is applied to the fund-raising projects of pupils in American Jewish religious schools.

Kes: A *Beta Esrael* (see above) high priest who is the spiritual leader of the community.

Ladino: A Judeo-Spanish language, usually written in Latin characters, spoken by many Sephardic groups. It contains Hebrew and Turkish, but it is basically Spanish.

Mesgid: The *Amharic* word for "synagogue." One of the huts serves as the synagogue, which is the center of religious life in the community.

Sanbat: The word for the Sabbath (Shabbat) in *Amharic.*

Sanbat Salaam: Amharic for "Sabbath of Peace," the traditional Sabbath greeting, equivalent to the Hebrew Shabbat Shalom.

Shalom Aleichem: Hebrew for "peace unto you."

Sheleg: Hebrew for "snow."

Tsedakah: The Hebrew word for "righteousness." It is the word used by Jews to signify "charity," the obligation to give to those who are needy and less fortunate.

Tukul: The *Amharic* word for a *Beta Esrael* hut. It is usually round and is covered over with a straw roof.

Yeshivot (Pl. of *yeshivah*): Schools for talmudic study.

Yiddish: A Judeo-German language, usually written in Hebrew characters, spoken by the Jews of Eastern Europe. It contains Hebrew and some Slavic, but it is basically German.